CONTENTS

Genie of
the Lamp

Miriam

Princess
Fatimah

CAST OF
CHARACTERS

CHAPTER 1:
"I can use him"

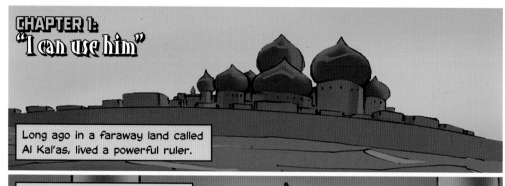

Long ago in a faraway land called Al Kal'as, lived a powerful ruler.

Sultan Shadid had more wives, riches, and power than the rest of his people combined.

He ruled Al Kal'as with the help of his Grand Vizier.

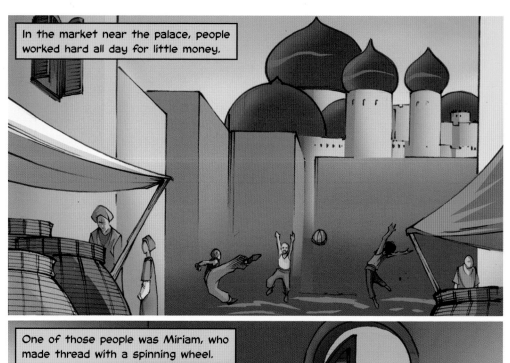

In the market near the palace, people worked hard all day for little money.

One of those people was Miriam, who made thread with a spinning wheel.

Her husband had died years earlier, leaving her to take care of their 10-year-old boy.

Their son, Aladdin, played in the streets all day while Miriam worked.

Most people thought he was a selfish, lazy child.

Until one day . . .

Hmm.

I can use him.

Who is that boy?

If you tell me everything you know about him, I'll give you a gold coin.

The child could not refuse and talked about Aladdin all day.

By nightfall, the stranger knew all he wanted.

9

Mother? This man needs to talk to you.

But I'm not in trouble. I promise!

Good morning, sir. May I help you?

I'm looking for this boy's father. Where is he?

I'm sorry, sir. My husband died many years ago.

Of course, the man was not Aladdin's uncle. He wasn't even from Al Kal'as.

He was actually a wicked sorcerer from Morocco.

Without knowing, Miriam and Aladdin invited the man to stay for dinner.

It was a basic meal, as they had little money.

This is no way for my brother's family to live. Don't you both work?

I do, but Aladdin is too lazy to work.

I have never been given a chance.

CHAPTER 2:
"Where's all the treasure?"

The next morning, Aladdin and the sorcerer set off.

They left Al Kal'as far behind.

They walked across the desert sands for many long hours.

Finally, the sorcerer stopped.

He drew a magical pattern in the sand.

Stand back, my boy!

Without a second thought, Aladdin leapt into the magical cavern.

And discovered . . .

An oasis!

There it is!

Aladdin was trapped.

Why bring me all this way for two pieces of cheap brass?

But when Aladdin put on the ring . . .

Where do you wish to go, oh Master?

When the ifrit disappeared, Aladdin woke his mother.

He told her about the ring, but she had other reasons to be happy.

CHAPTER 3

"What is your wish?"

Weeks went by, and Aladdin and Miriam saw no more of the sorcerer.

Life went back to normal.

Aladdin kept the ifrit's ring hidden in his pocket.

He tried to find work, but no one would give him a job.

I don't need any lazy kids around here!

Just give me a chance, sir.

23

Soon, Aladdin and his mother were out of money again.

The ifrit of the ring can take me anywhere.

I could appear in the fruit seller's stall, Mother.

I could take food without anyone knowing!

No! We're not thieves! We'll just have to sell something.

How about that old lamp you found?

If I clean it up a bit, someone might buy it.

RUB

RUB

RUB

RUB

RUB

27

The next day, Aladdin headed to the market with one of the golden plates.

See you soon, Mother!

This plate has to be worth something.

He sold the dish to the first merchant who would buy it.

If you have more, I'll buy them!

Mother will be so proud of me. We'll never go hungry again!

Aladdin had outgrown his boyhood ways.

See you tomorrow, sir! I'll be here bright and early.

Eventually, Aladdin no longer needed the magic lamp . . .

Where have you been all day, my son?

I found a job, Mother, and it pays an honest wage.

I'm so proud of you, Aladdin!

We finally have everything we've always wanted.

But soon, Aladdin wanted something more . . .

CHAPTER 4

"From love"

33

That night . . .

Mother, have you ever seen Princess Fatimah?

Of course not.

The sultan doesn't like common people looking at her.

Why not?

She's his only child. He does all he can to protect her.

From what?

From love.

Aladdin didn't understand his mother's answer, but Miriam would say no more.

After dinner, Aladdin went up to the rooftop to think . . .

. . . and make a decision.

I haven't forgotten about you, old friend.

Where do you wish to go, Master?

Take me to Princess Fatimah's room in the palace.

I want to know why the sultan won't let people see her.

Easily done.

SNAP!

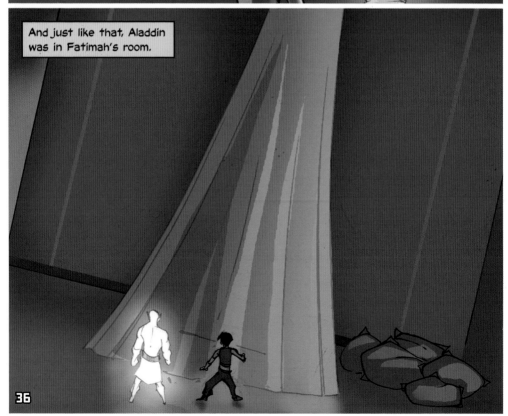

And just like that, Aladdin was in Fatimah's room.

Quietly, he walked to her bedside and drew back the canopy.

!

Aladdin was in love.

We should leave before someone finds you here, Master.

You're right. Take me home.

SNAP!

Easily done.

The next morning . . .

You did what?!

You're lucky nobody saw you!

CHAPTER 5:
"A bowl of fruit?"

So what does the princess look like?

She's beautiful. I want to marry her, Mother.

Don't be foolish! The sultan will never agree to that.

I think I can convince him.

The following day, Miriam went to Sultan Shadid's palace.

She says her name is Miriam. I've never seen her before.

What do you want, old woman?

Your Highness, my son wishes to marry your daughter.

He asked me to bring you this bowl of fruit to convince you.

HA!

HA!

HA!

A bowl of fruit for my daughter?

HA!

HA!

HA!

HA!

39

41

The next day, Miriam did as Aladdin said.

Sultan Shadid!

As soon as she greeted the sultan, someone ran into the throne room.

Sultan Shadid!

What is the meaning of this?

You have to look outside, your Highness . . . !

43

That is my son.

Oh my!

That morning, Aladdin had asked his genie to create the parade.

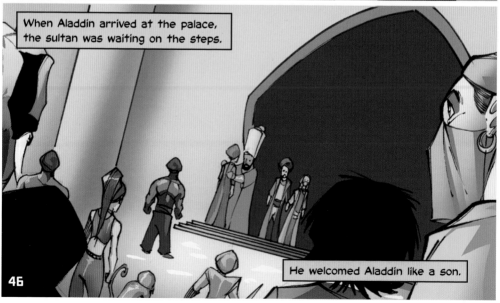

When Aladdin arrived at the palace, the sultan was waiting on the steps.

He welcomed Aladdin like a son.

Aladdin and Fatimah were married that very day.

The next evening, Aladdin and his mother came to live in the palace.

Aladdin already knew he loved Fatimah.

Soon she fell in love with him, too.

He never told her about his magic lamp . . .

. . . but keeping it a secret nearly ruined everything.

47

CHAPTER 6:
"New lamps for old"

Over the years, Aladdin had forgotten all about the sorcerer who lied to him.

Yet, the sorcerer had not forgotten the lamp.

Then one night . . .

The sorcerer cast a spell to call forth Aladdin's ghost.

But the spell didn't work.

Aladdin must be alive!

The lamp must work!

It's the only way that brat could have escaped!

Fuelled by anger, the sorcerer hurried towards Al Kal'as to find Aladdin.

The next day, he broke into Aladdin's old home.

But no one lived there anymore.

Where could he be?!

Excuse me. Have you seen the boy who used to live here?

Aladdin? He lives at the palace now. He's married to Princess Fatimah.

He must have my lamp!

The sorcerer quickly came up with a plan, buying every gold lamp he could afford.

Yes! I'll take them all!

Certainly, sir!

Next he bought a cart, put his lamps inside, and pushed it to the palace.

New lamps for old!

Princess? There's a man outside trading new lamps for old ones.

51

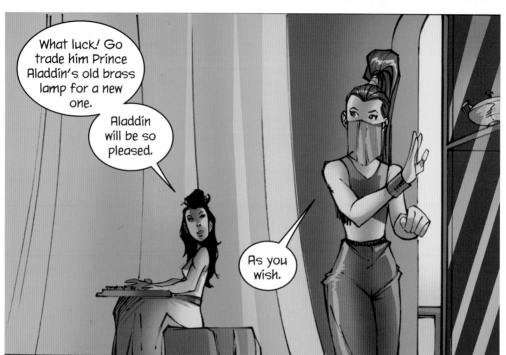

Unfortunately, Aladdin was away on a hunting trip with the sultan.

Worse, he'd never told Fatimah about the lamp.

53

CHAPTER 7:
"You've had your fun!"

And just like that, the genie lifted the palace right off the ground.

He shook out everyone except Princess Fatimah.

With the sorcerer on his shoulder, he flew away with the palace.

That night, Aladdin and the sultan returned.

What happened here? Where is the palace and my wife?!

Aladdin found a quiet place and took the ifrit's ring from his pocket.

Aladdin told the genie to take the palace back to Al Kal'as.

The people of Morocco were glad to see it go . . .

. . . and the people of Al Kal'as were glad to get it back.

Miriam and Fatimah rushed up when Aladdin returned.

They all had a long talk.

They agreed to keep no more secrets and to always share the lamp.

From that day on, they used it only for the good of Al Kal'as.

As for the sorcerer, who'd caused so much trouble . . .

Aladdin made sure he couldn't hurt anyone ever again.

Curse you, Aladdin! You haven't heard the last of me!

63

NIGHTS

The story of "Aladdin and the Magic Lamp" is part of a collection of Middle Eastern and South Asian folktales known as *One Thousand and One Nights*. These tales have been passed down from generation to generation for hundreds of years. The first English-language edition, entitled *Arabian Nights' Entertainments*, was published in 1706.

Since then, many versions of the book have been published – some containing more than 1,000 stories. In each of these editions, the tales of mystery and adventure are told by the same narrator, a beautiful woman named Scheherazade. She has just married an evil ruler who plans to kill her before the night is through. To stop him, Scheherazade entertains the king with a new story each night, and he soon forgets about his deadly plan.

The Arabian Nights tales remain some of the greatest stories ever told. They include popular adventures, such as "The Fisherman and the Genie", "The Seven Voyages of Sinbad", and "Ali Baba and the Forty Thieves". Many of these stories have been adapted into films, books, and plays, which are still popular today.

ALADDIN FACTS

Like many of the Arabian Nights tales, the first person to tell the story of Aladdin is unknown. The story became popular in Europe when it was translated into French by Antoine Galland in the early 1700s. He claimed to have heard the tale from a Syrian storyteller named Hanna Diab.

"Aladdin and his Magic Lamp" is one of the most popular Arabian Nights tales. In 1992, it became a blockbuster hit for Walt Disney Studios. Shortly after the film's release, *Aladdin* became the highest-grossing animated film up to that time.

That year, Disney's *Aladdin* received two Academy Awards, including Best Song and Best Original Score. The song "A Whole New World" also won a Grammy Award that same year.

ABOUT THE AUTHOR

Carl Bowen is a writer and editor who lives in Georgia, USA. He was born in Louisiana, lived briefly in England, and was raised in Georgia where he attended school and college. He has published a handful of novels and more than a dozen short stories, all while working at White Wolf Publishing as an editor and advertising copywriter. His first graphic novel, published by Udon Entertainment, is called *Exalted*.

ABOUT THE ILLUSTRATOR

Alfonso Ruiz was born in 1975 in Macuspana, Tabasco, in Mexico, where the temperature is just as hot as the sauce is. He became a comic book illustrator when he was 17 years old and has worked on many graphic novels since then. Alfonso has illustrated several English graphic novels, including retellings of *Dracula* and *Pinocchio*.

GLOSSARY

ashamed feeling of embarrassment or guilt

canopy piece of cloth or other material, often covering a bed

cavern large cave

ifrit powerful, supernatural creature often found in Arabic and Islamic folktales

genie magic spirit that serves the person who calls it

Grand Vizier chief officer of state in some Muslim countries, such as the old Turkish empire

market place where people buy and sell food and goods

merchant someone who sells goods for profit

Morocco country in northwest Africa, bordering the Atlantic Ocean and the Mediterranean Sea

oasis place in the desert where there is water and plants and trees

sorcerer someone who performs magic by controlling evil spirits, often referred to as a wizard

sultan emperor or ruler of some Muslim countries

wage money someone is paid for his or her work

DISCUSSION QUESTIONS

1. The genie can fulfill any wish. If you had a magic lamp, what three things would you ask for?

2. Aladdin didn't tell Princess Fatimah about the magic lamp. Why do you think he made this decision? Is it ever okay to withhold the truth from someone? Explain.

3. At the end of the story, the evil sorcerer promises to seek revenge against Aladdin. Do you think Aladdin will have to face him again? Why or why not?

WRITING PROMPTS

1. If you had a magic ring that could take you anywhere in the world, where would you go? Describe the place, and then write a story about your adventure there.

2. Do you think Aladdin and Princess Fatimah will live happily ever after? Write another chapter to this book. What adventures will they have next? Will they ever use the magic lamp again?

3. Imagine your own Arabian Nights tale. Think of a story filled with mystery and adventure. Then write it down and read it to friends and family.

ARABIAN NIGHTS TALES

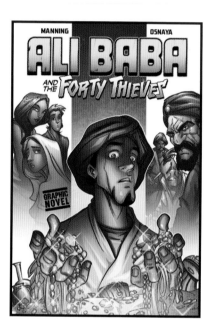

ALADDIN AND THE MAGIC LAMP

The legendary tale of Aladdin, a poor youth living in the city of Al Kal'as. One day, the crafty boy outsmarts an evil sorcerer, getting his hands on a magical lamp that houses a wish-fulfilling genie! Soon, all of Aladdin's dreams come true, and he finds himself married to a beautiful princess. All is well until, one day, the evil sorcerer returns to reclaim the lamp.

ALI BABA AND THE FORTY THIEVES

The legendary tale of Ali Baba, a young Persian boy who discovers a cave filled with gold and jewels, the hidden treasures of 40 deadly thieves. Unfortunately, his greedy brother, Kasim, cannot wait to get his hands on the riches. Returning to the cave, he is captured by the thieves and killed, and now the evil men want revenge on Ali Baba as well.

THE SEVEN VOYAGES OF SINBAD

The tale of Sinbad the Sailor, who goes to sea in search of great riches and discovers even greater adventures. On his seven treacherous voyages, the Persian explorer braves a shipwreck, fights off savage cannibals, and battles a giant Cyclops, hoping to survive and tell his legendary story.

THE FISHERMAN AND THE GENIE

The legendary tale of an evil Persian king, who marries a new wife each day and then kills her the next morning. To stop this murderous ruler, a brave woman named Scheherazade risks her own life and marries the king herself . . . but not without a plan. On their wedding night, she will entertain him with the tale of the Fisherman and the Genie – a story so amazing, he'll never want it to end.